Great Songs

Exclusively sold and distributed by

HAL LEONARD EUROPE
Hal Leonard Europe is a joint venture between
Hal Leonard Corporation and Music Sales Limited

Published by Hal Leonard.

Order No. HLE90004607
ISBN 978-1-78038-886-1

Printed in the EU.

Best Thing I Never Had

Words & Music by Kenneth Edmonds, Antonio Dixon, Patrick Smith,
Beyoncé Knowles, Larry Griffin, Caleb McCampbell & Robert Taylor

B F♯ D♯m 6fr C♯ 4fr B F♯
a time I thought that you did
(2.) you're hurt. Boo hoo. Oh, did you ex-
D♯m 6fr C♯ 4fr B F♯ D♯m 6fr C♯ 4fr
ev - 'ry - thing right. No lies, no wrong. Boy, I
-pect me to care? You don't de - serve my tears.
B F♯ D♯m 6fr C♯ 4fr
must have been out of my mind. So when I
I guess that's why they ain't there. When I think that
G♯m7 4fr D♯m7 6fr C♯ 4fr G♯m7 4fr
think of the time that I al - most loved you,
there was a time that I al - most loved you,
you showed your ass and I,

Bm(maj7)
G♯m
4fr
F♯/A♯
I saw the re - al you.
Thank God you blew it,
thank God I dodged the bul - let.
I'm so
B
C♯sus4
o - ver you,
so ba - by good look - in' out.
I want - ed you bad.
F♯
B
D♯m
6fr
C♯
4fr
F♯
B
I'm so through with it.
'Cause hon - est - ly you turned out to be the...
3
D♯m
6fr
C♯
4fr
F♯
B
D♯m
6fr
C♯
4fr
You turned out to be the...
And I'm
(Best thing I nev - er had.)
(Best thing I nev - er had.)
3

F♯
B
D♯m
C♯
Bmaj9
To Coda
4fr
6fr
gon' al - ways be the...
(Best thing you nev - er had.)
I bet it
3
1.
2.
sucks to be you right now.
2. So sad.
D♯m
Bm/D
I know you want me back.
It's times to face the facts, that
C♯
G♯/B♯
I'm the one that's got a - way.
Lord knows that it would take an - oth - er

Badd9
2fr
F♯/A♯
place, an - oth - er time, an - oth - er world, an - oth - er life. Thank
G♯m7
4fr
F♯/A♯
Badd9
2fr
D.S. al Coda
God I found the good in good - bye. I used to want you so bad.
Coda
Bmaj9
Best thing you nev - er had. I used to want you so bad.
F♯
B
D♯m
6fr
C♯
4fr
I'm so through with that. 'Cause hon - est - ly you

F♯ B D♯m C♯ F♯ B
6fr 4fr
turned out to be the... You turned out to be the...
(Best thing I nev - er had.)
D♯m C♯ F♯ B D♯m C♯
6fr 4fr 6fr 4fr
And I will nev - er be the...
(Best thing I nev - er had.) (Best thing you nev - er had.)
Bmaj9 C♯
4fr
Oh, ba - by, I bet it sucks to be you right now.
3

F♯
B
D♯m
C♯/E♯
F♯
B
6fr
Goes a - round, comes back a - round.
(Goes a - round, comes back a - round.)
Bet it
D♯m
C♯
F♯
B
D♯m
C♯/E♯
6fr
4fr
6fr
sucks to be you right now.
(Goes a - round comes back a - round.)
Bet it sucks to be you right now.
rit.
F♯
B
D♯m
C♯
F♯
6fr
4fr
(Goes a - round comes back a - round.)
Bet it sucks to be you right now.

Can't Take My Eyes Off Of You

Words & Music by Bob Crewe & Bob Gaudio

Fm6
C
love has ar - rived
and I thank God I'm a - live.
You're just
D/C
Dm7b5/C
C
too good to be true,
can't take my eyes
off you.
2. Par - don the
C
Cmaj7
way that I stare
there's noth - ing else
to com - pare.
(Verse 3 see block lyrics)
C7
The sight of
you leaves me weak,
there are no

F
Fm6
words left to speak. But if you feel like I feel, please let me
C
D7/C
know that it's real. You're just too good to be true,
Dm7b5/C
C
can't take my eyes off you.
1º only
Dm7
G7
C6

Dm7
G7
C6
A7♯9
To Coda
Dm9
3fr
G13
3fr
G9
3fr
I love you ba - by and if it's quite al - right I need you
Em7
Am11
5fr
Am7
Dm7
ba - by to warm the lone - ly night I love you ba - by
G9sus4
G7
Cmaj9
A9sus4
A9
6fr
Dm9
3fr
trust in me when I say. Oh, pret - ty ba - by don't bring me

G13
G9
3fr
Em7
Am11
5fr
Am7
down I pray oh, pret - ty ba - by now that I've found you stay and let me
Dm7
G9sus4
D.S. al Coda
love you ba - by, let me love you. 3. You're just
Coda
Dm9
ba - by and if it's quite al- right I need you ba - by to warm the
G7
Cmaj9
lone - ly night I love you ba - by trust in me when I say,

Verse 3:

You're just too good to be true,
Can't take my eyes off you.
You'd be like heaven to touch,
I wanna hold you so much.
At long last love has arrived,
And I thank God I'm alive.
You're just too good to be true,
Can't take my eyes off you.

I love you baby *etc.*

Crazy Little Thing Called Love

Words & Music by Freddie Mercury

G
C
G/B
I must get round to it, I ain't
D
B♭
C
To Coda
D
read - y. Cra - zy lit - tle thing called love.
This thing (This thing.) called love (Called love.) it cries
G
C
G/B
D
(Like a ba - by.) in a cra - dle all night. It swings (Woo woo.) it jives

G
C
G/B
(Woo woo.) it shakes all o - ver like a jel - ly fish, I kind - a
D
B♭
C
D
like it. Cra - zy lit - tle thing called love.
G
There goes my ba - by, she
C
G
B♭
knows how to rock 'n' roll. She drives me cra - zy

E
A
F
she gives me hot and cold fe - ver, then she leaves me in a cool, cool sweat.
N.C.
E
A
I got - ta be cool
D
G
re - lax, get hip, get
C
G
D
on my tracks, take a back seat, hitch - hike, and

G
C
G
D
take a long ride on my mot - or - bike___ un - til I'm read - y
(2º only) (Read - y Fred - die.)
B♭
C
D
1.
2.
D.S. al Coda
cra - zy lit - tle thing called love.___
There goes my
This thing_
Coda
D
B♭
C
D
Repeat to fade
Cra - zy lit - tle thing called love.___

Dream A Little Dream Of Me

Words by Gus Kahn
Music by Wilbur Schwandt & Fabian Andre

C
E♭dim
A♭6
G
C
G/B
Say "Night - ie night" and kiss me, just hold me tight and
A7
Dm
tell me you'll miss me, while I'm a - lone and
Fm
C
A♭7
G7
C
E7
4fr
3fr
blue as can be dream a lit - tle dream of me.
A
F♯m
Bm
E
A
F♯m
Stars fad - ing but I lin - ger on, dear, still crav - ing your

Bsus4
E
A
F#m
kiss.
I'm longing to
lin-ger till dawn dear, just say-ing this.
Ab7
G7
C
Ebdim
Ab6
G
Sweet dreams till sun-beams find you,
G/B
A7
Dm
sweet dreams that leave all wor-ries be-hind you, but in your dreams what-

To Coda
Fm
C
A♭7
4fr
G7
3fr
-ev - er they be,
dream a lit - tle dream of me,
C
G
C
E♭dim
A♭6
G
ba ba ba.
C
G/B
A7
A7sus4
A7
Dm
Fm
C
A♭7
4fr
C
E7
D.S. al Coda

Coda
C
E♭dim
Fm
G
ba da da da da da da.
Da ba ba
ba ba ba ba. Doo ba ba ba ba ba la da da la da da da.
Sweet dreams till sun - beams find you.
Sweet dreams all wor - ries be - hind you.
But in your dreams what - ev - er they be, dream a lit - tle dream of me.
Sweet dreams.
Repeat to fade

The Fear

Words & Music by Lily Allen & Greg Kurstin

F/E♭
B♭/D
B♭m/D♭
and fuck loads of dia - monds, I heard peo - ple die while they're try - ing to find
- ter 'cause I'm pack ing plas - tic, and that's what makes my life so fuck-ing fan - tas -
F
F/E♭
B♭/D
them. And I'll take my clothes off and it will be shame - less, 'cause ev - 'ry - one knows
- tic. And I am a wea - pon of mas - sive con - sump - tion and it's not my fault

B♭m/D♭
F
F/E♭
it's how you get fam - ous. I'll look at the Sun and I'll look in the Mir-
it's how I'm pro - grammed to func - tion. I'll look at the Sun and I'll look in the Mir-

B♭/D
B♭m/D♭
N.C.
F
-ror. I'm on the right track, yeah, I'm on - to a win - ner.
-ror. I'm on the right track, yeah, I'm on - to a win - ner.
And I don't know
Dm
Am
what's right and what's real an - y - more.
F
Dm
E♭
6fr
And I don't know how I'm meant to feel an - y - more.
F
Dm
When do you think it will all be - come

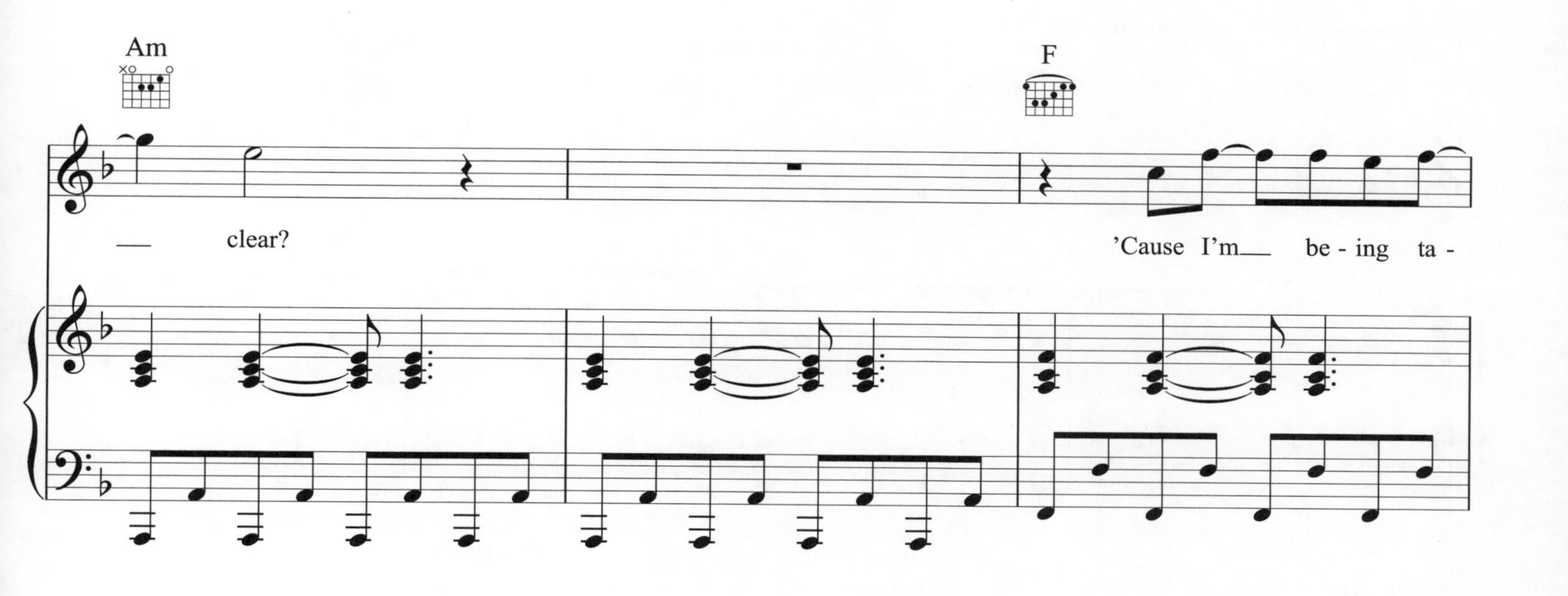
Am
F
clear?
'Cause I'm be - ing ta -

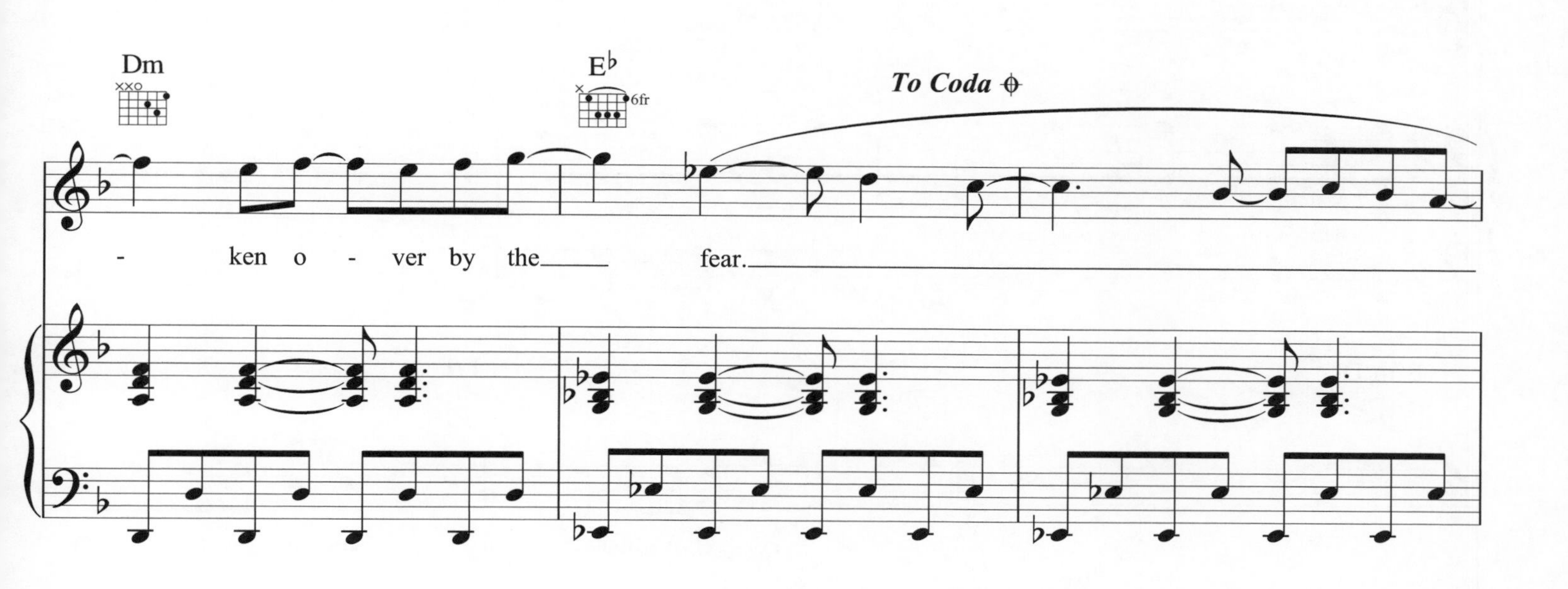
Dm
E♭
6fr
To Coda
- ken o - ver by the fear.

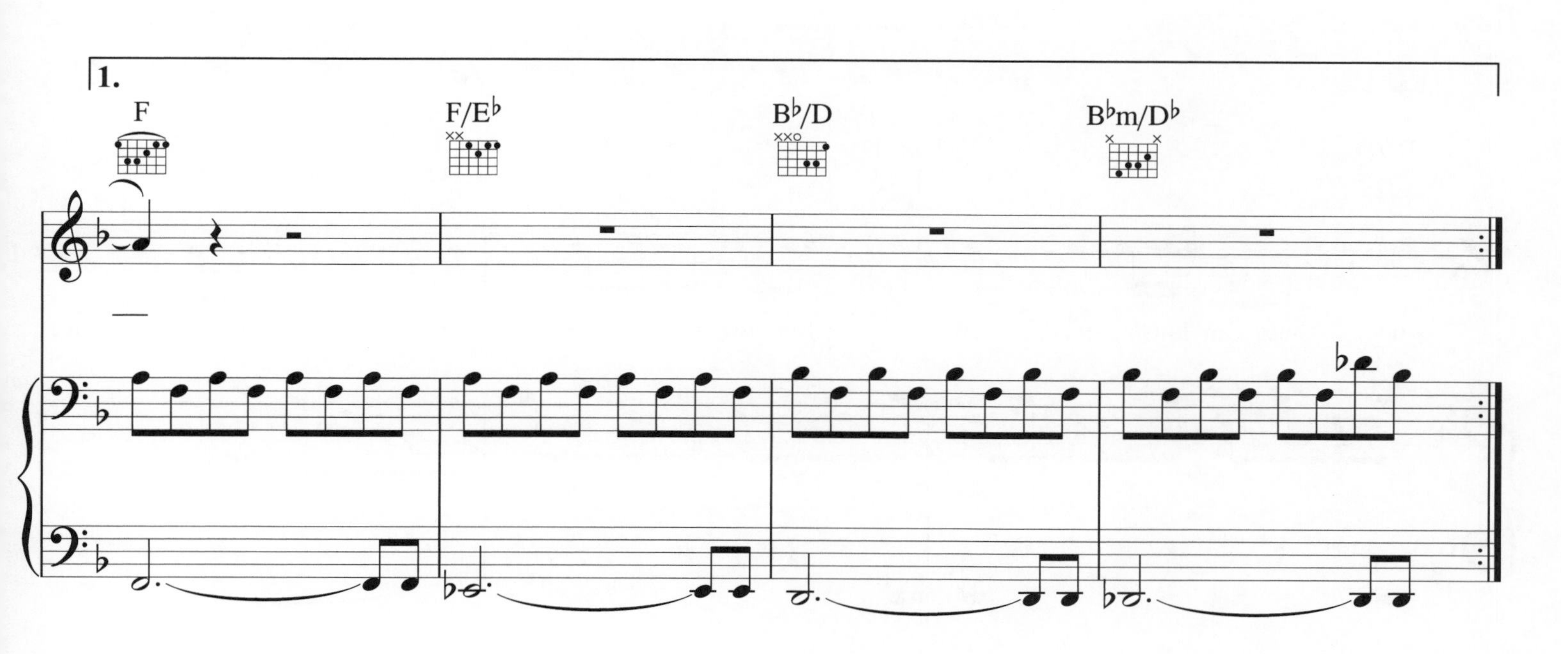
1.
F
F/E♭
B♭/D
B♭m/D♭

2.
F
F/E♭
B♭/D
B♭m/D♭
F
F/E♭
B♭/D
B♭m/D♭
F
F/E♭
For - get a - bout guns and for - get am - u - ni -
B♭/D
B♭m/D♭
F
- tion, 'cause I'm kill - ing them all on my own lit - tle mis - sion. Now, I'm not a saint,

F/E♭
B♭/D
B♭m/D♭
but I'm not a sin - ner, and ev - 'ry - thing's cool as long as I'm get - ting thin -
D.S. al Coda
Coda
F
E♭
6fr
- ner. And I don't know
F
Dm
Am
F
Dm
E♭
6fr

Fast Car

Words & Music by Tracy Chapman

Dmaj7
A5
5fr
F♯m
Eadd4
An - y - place is bet - ter.
Won't have to drive too far,
Start - ing from ze - ro, got noth - ing to lose.
just cross the bor - der and in - to the cit - y.
May - be we'll make some - thing,
You and I can both get jobs and
but me my - self, I got noth - ing to prove.
fin - 'ly see what it means to be liv - ing.
1.
2.
3. See,

Dmaj7
A5
5fr
F♯m
Eadd4
my old man's got a prob - lem. He live with the bot - tle that's the way it is. He says his
(Verses 4 & 5 see block lyrics)
bod - y's too old for work - ing. His bod - y's too young to look like his. My
ma - ma went off and left him. She want - ed more from life than he could give. I said
some - bod - y's got to take care of him. So I quit school and that's what I did.

1º only
Dmaj7
A5
5fr
F♯m
Eadd4
You got a fast car, but is it fast e - nough so we can fly a - way?
We got - ta make a de - ci - sion: leave to - night or live and die this way.
'Cause I re - mem - ber we were

D
A
driv - ing, driv-ing in your car, the speed so fast it felt like I was drunk.
F♯m
E
Cit - y lights lay out be - fore us and your arm felt nice wrapped 'round my shoul - der. And
D
F♯m
E
I had a feel - ing that I be - longed. And
D
F♯m
E
I had a feel - ing I could be some - one,

1, 2.
D
E
Dmaj7
A5
5fr
be some - one, be some - one.
F♯m
Eadd4
Dmaj7
A5
5fr
F♯m
Eadd4
3.
Dmaj7
A5
5fr
F♯m
Eadd4
Dmaj7
A5
5fr
F♯m
Eadd4
Dmaj7
A5
5fr
F♯m
Eadd4
You got a fast car, but is it fast e - nough so we can fly a - way?

Verse 4:
You got a fast car and we go cruising to entertain ourselves.
You still ain't got a job.
Now I work in a market as a checkout girl.
I know things will get better.
You'll find work and I'll get promoted.
We'll move out of the shelter,
Buy a big house and live in the suburbs.

Verse 5:
You got a fast car, and I got a job that pays all our bills.
You stay out drinking late at the bar,
See more of your friends than you do of your kids.
I'd always hoped for better,
Thought maybe together you and me would find it.
I got no plans, I ain't going nowhere,
So take your fast car and keep on driving.

Go Your Own Way

Words & Music by Lindsey Buckingham

Fadd9
If I could, may-be I'd give
If I could, ba-by, I'd give
Csus4
C
B♭
you my world.
you my world.
How can I
O-pen up,
Fadd9
F
when you won't take it from me?
ev-'ry-thing's wait-ing for you.
Dm
B♭
C
You can go your own way!
Go

Dm
B♭
your own way.
You can call it an - oth -
C
Dm
er lone - ly day.
You can go
B♭
1, 2.
C
your own way!
Go your own way.
3.
C
Dm
Go your own way.
You can call

B♭
C
it an - oth - er lone - ly day.
Dm
B♭
C
Dm
B♭
C
Dm
B♭
C

Dm
B♭
C
Dm
B♭
C
Dm
B♭
C
You can go your own way!
Dm
B♭
C
Repeat and fade
You can call it an - oth - er lone-ly day.

Have I Told You Lately

Words & Music by Van Morrison

Emaj7
A/B
E
G♯m7
4fr
Aadd9
A/B
B
1, 3, 5. Have I told you late - ly that I love you?
(2.) morn - ing sun in all it's glo - ry
4° Piano solo till *
E
G♯m7
Aadd9
B
Have I told you there's no - one a - bove you?
greets the day with hope and com - fort too
Amaj7
G♯m7
Fill my heart with glad - ness, take a - way my sad - ness,
and you fill my life with laugh - ter, you can make it bet - ter,
1, 3.
F♯m7
A/B
E
A/B
ease my trou - bles that's what you do.
2. Oh the

2, 4.
E
F#m7
G#m7
4fr
Amaj7
do.
*
There's a love that's di - vine
G#m7
4fr
and it's yours and it's mine, like the sun.
A
At the end of the day
3
3
G#m7
4fr
A/B
3
we should give thanks and pray to the One.
3, 5. Have I
3
3
3

5.
E
F#m7
G#m7
4fr
Amaj7
3
do.
1. Take a - way my sad - ness,
2. Fill my heart with glad - ness,
G#m7
4fr
F#m7
A/B
fill my life with glad - ness,
take a - way my sad - ness,
ease my trou - bles that's what you
1.
E
F#m7
E/G#
2.
Eadd9
do.
do.

Hey, Soul Sister

Words & Music by Espen Lind, Patrick Monahan
& Amund Bjoerklund

E
B
-get you and so I went and let you blow my mind.
-rec - tion, a game show love con - nec - tion we can't de - ny.
C♯m
4fr
A
B
Your
I'm
E
B
sweet moon - beam, the smell of you in ev - 'ry
so ob - sessed. My heart is bound to beat right
C♯m
4fr
A
sin - gle dream I dream. I knew when we col -
out my un - trimmed chest. I be - lieve in

E
B
-li - ded you're the one I have de - ci - ded who's one of my kind.
you, like a vir - gin, you're Ma - don - na. And I'm al - ways gon - na
C♯m
4fr
A
B
wan - na blow your mind.
A
B
E
B
A
Hey soul sis - ter, ain't that Mis - ter Mis - ter on the ra - di - o, ste - re - o? The way
B
E
B
A
B
E
B
you move ain't fair you know. Hey soul sis - ter, I don't wan - na miss a sin - gle

1.
A
B
N.C.
E
thing you do
to-night.
Hey,
B
C♯m
4fr
A
hey,
hey.
2.
E
B
The way you can cut a rug.
Watch-ing you is the on-ly drug I
C♯m
4fr
A/C♯
need. So gang-ster, I'm so thug. You're the on-ly one I'm dream-ing of. You see

E/B
B
I can be my - self now fi - nal - ly. In fact there's noth - ing I can't be.
C♯m
4fr
B
A
I want the world to see you be - ing with me.
E
Hey soul sis - ter, ain't that Mis - ter Mis - ter on the ra - di - o, ste - re - o? The way
you move ain't fair you know. Hey soul sis - ter, I don't wan - na miss a sin - gle

A
B
A
thing you do to - night.
Hey soul sis - ter, I
B
E
B
A
B
don't wan-na miss a sin-gle thing you do
to - night.
E
B
C#m
4fr
Hey,
hey,
hey.
1.
2.
A
A/B
A
B
E
to - night.
to - night.

I'm Not In Love

Words & Music by Eric Stewart & Graham Gouldman

F/A
A7
Dm
it's just a sil - ly phase I'm go - ing through.
B♭
B♭m
6fr
And just be - cause I call you up,
F/A
A7
Dm
don't get me wrong, don't think you've got it made.
B♭
C
C7
F
B♭
I'm not in love, no, no!
It's be - cause...

B♭11
B♭
I like to see you
B♭m
6fr
F/A
A7
but then a - gain,
that does - n't mean you mean that
Dm
B♭
B♭m
6fr
much to me.
So if I call you,
don't make a
F/A
A7
Dm
fuss,
don't tell your friends a - bout the two of us.

B♭
C
I'm not in love, no, no!
C7
F
5fr
N.C.
It's be - cause...
f

F6
Be quiet, big boys don't cry. Big boys don't cry. Big boys don't cry. Big boys don't
cry. Big boys don't cry. Big boys don't cry.
pp
A7
B♭
I keep your
B♭m
F/A
pic - ture up - on the wall, it hides a

A7
Dm
B♭
nas - ty stain that's ly - ing there.
So don't you
B♭m
6fr
F/A
ask me to give it back.
I know you know it
A7
Dm
B♭
does - n't mean that much to me.
I'm not in
C(add9)
C7
F
love, no, no!
It's be - cause...
3

B♭m7
E♭7
6fr
A♭
4fr
Fm7
A♭/E♭
4fr
Ooh, you'll wait a long time for me.
B♭m7
E♭7
6fr
F11
1.
F
Ooh, you'll wait a long time.
2.
F
B♭
B♭m
6fr
I'm not in love, so don't for-
F/A
A7
Dm
-get it, it's just a sil - ly phase I'm go - ing through.

B♭
B♭m
And just be - cause
I call you
F/A
A7
Dm
up,
don't get me wrong, don't think you've got it made.
B♭
B♭m
I'm not in love,
I'm not in love.
C11
C
Repeat 14 times and fade

Maggie May

Words & Music by Rod Stewart & Martin Quittenton

A
5fr
G
3fr
It's late Sep - tem - ber and I real - ly should be back
But that don't wor - ry me none, in my eyes you're
But you turned in - to a lov - er and moth - er, what a lov - er, you wore
D
5fr
G
3fr
at school.
ev - 'ry - thing.
me out.
I know I keep you a - mused
I laugh at all of your jokes,
All you did was wreck my bed,
3
D
5fr
G
3fr
A
5fr
but I feel I'm be - ing used.
my love you did - n't need to coax.
and in the morn - ing, kick me in the head.
Oh,

Em
7fr
F♯m
9fr
Em
7fr
Mag - gie, I could - n't have tried any - y - more.
D/F♯
7fr
Em
7fr
A
5fr
You led me a - way from home just to
°3 'cause you
Em
7fr
A
5fr
Em
7fr
save you from be - ing a - lone.
didn't wan - na be a - lone.
You stole my heart and that's
You stole my soul and that's
You stole my heart, I could - n't
A
5fr
D
5fr
1, 2, 3.
what real - ly hurts.
a pain I can do with - out.
leave you if I tried.
2. The

4.
Em
A
5fr
3
(Guitar)
D
5fr
G
5fr
Em
G
5fr
G/A
5fr
D
5fr
A
5fr
G
5fr
D
5fr
4. I sup - pose I could col - lect my books and get on back to school,

A
5fr
G
3fr
or steal my dad - dy's cue and make a liv - ing out of
D
5fr
G
3fr
play - ing pool. Or find my - self a rock 'n' roll
D
5fr
G
3fr
A
5fr
band that needs a help - ing hand. Oh,
Em
7fr
F♯m
9fr
Em
7fr
Mag - gie I wish I'd nev - er seen your face.
3

D/F♯
Em
A
7fr
5fr
You made a first class fool out of me but I'm as
Em
A
Em
blind as a fool can be.
You stole my heart but I
A
D
love you an - y - way.
Em
A
D
G
3fr
(Guitar)
3

1.
2.
Em
G
G/A
D
D6/9
G/D
Em7add11
7fr
3fr
5fr
4fr
3
Play 4 times ad lib.
Play 5 times
ad lib. to fade
Mag - gie,
I
wish I'd
nev
-
er seen_ your
face.

My Girl

Words & Music by William "Smokey" Robinson & Ronald White

C
F
C
Dm
month of May.
I guess
F
G
C
Dm
F
G
you say, what can make me feel this way?
C
Dm
To Coda
My girl. (My girl, my girl.) Talk - ing 'bout my girl.
C/G
G7
N.C.
Dm
G7
C
F
My Girl! I've got so much hon - ey the bees en - vy

C
F
C
me.
I've got a sweet-er song
F
C
F
D.S. al Coda
than the birds in the tree.
Well,
Coda
C/D G7/D N.C. Dm G7 N.C.
My girl!
C
F

C
F
Dm
G
G/F
Em
A
D
I don't need no mon - ey,
G
D
G
for - tune or fame.
I got
D
G
D
all the rich - es, ba - by one man can claim.

G
D
Em
G
A
Well, I guess you say,
D
Em
G
A
D
what can make me feel this way?
My girl. (My girl,
Em
D/A
A7
G
F♯m
A/E
my girl.) Talk-ing 'bout my girl.
My girl! Talk-ing 'bout
Repeat ad lib. to fade
Dmaj7
Em7
A
G
F♯m
A/E
my girl.
Talk-ing 'bout

Patience

Words & Music by Mark Owen, Gary Barlow,
Jason Orange, Howard Donald & John Shanks

E♭add9
F
Gm
B♭
5fr
3fr
but an - y min - ute all the pain will stop.
the one that I can al - ways de - pend.
Just hold me close in - side
I'll try to be strong, be - lieve me
B♭/D
C7
your arms to - night, don't be too hard on my e - mo - tions.
I'm try - ing to move on. It's com - pli - ca - ted but un - der - stand me.
'Cause
6fr
I need time.

B♭ F Gm E♭ B♭ F
3fr 6fr
My heart is numb, has no feel-ing, so while I'm still heal-ing, just
Gm E♭ 1. B♭ F 2. B♭ F
3fr 6fr
try 2. and have a lit-tle and have a lit-tle
A♭ E♭ B♭ A♭ E♭
4fr 6fr 4fr 6fr
pa - tience, yeah. Have a lit-tle pa - tience, yeah.
B♭ E♭ B♭/D Cm B♭
6fr 3fr
'Cause the scars run so deep, it's been hard, but I have to be - lieve.

F/A
F7/C
Have a lit - tle
Gm
E♭
B♭
F
pa - tience;
have a lit-tle
pa - tience.
Whoa,
'cause
I
I just need
time.
My heart is numb, has no feel - ing, so
3fr
6fr

B♭
F
Gm
3fr
E♭
6fr
while I'm still heal-ing, just try and have a lit-tle
pa - tience; have a lit-tle pa - tience.
My heart is numb, has no feel-ing, so while I'm still heal-ing, just
try and have a lit-tle pa - tience

Rehab

Words & Music by Amy Winehouse

C7
F7
C7
tried to make me go to re - hab, I won't go, go, go.
*
Em
RH alternative accompaniment, vamp following chords
Am
1. I'd rath - er be at home with Ray,
2. The man said, "Why do you think you here?"
3. I don't nev-er want to drink a-gain,
3
3
F
A♭
4fr
I ain't got se - ven-ty days,
I said I got no i - dea.
I just, ooh I just need a friend,
3
3

Em
'cause there's noth - ing, there's noth - ing you can
I'm gon - na, I'm gon - na lose my ba-
I'm not gon - na spend
3
Am
F
teach me, that I can't learn
- by, so I
ten weeks, have ev - 'ry - one
A♭
4fr
from Mis - ter Hath - a - way,
al - ways keep a bot - tle near,
think I'm on the mend,

G7
3fr
did - n't get a lot in class, but I
he said, "I just think you're de-pressed."
it's not just my pride,
F7
1, 2, 3.
know it don't come in a shot glass.
This me, "Yeah, ba - by, and the rest." They
it's just till these tears have
4.
C7
dried. They tried to make me go to re - hab, I said,

no, no, no. Yes I've been black but when
I come back, no, no, no, no.
G7
F7
I ain't got the time, and if my dad-dy thinks I'm fine, they
C7
F7
C7
N.C.
tried to make me go to re - hab, I won't go, go, go.

Rolling In The Deep

Words & Music by Adele Adkins & Paul Epworth

C5
3fr
G5
3fr
Fin - al - ly I can see you crys - tal clear.
There's a fire start - ing in my heart,
B♭5
G5
3fr
B♭5
Go a - head and sell me out and I'll lay your shit bare.
reach - ing a fe - ver pitch and it's bring - ing me out the dark.
cont. sim.
A♭
4fr
B♭
Gm7
3fr
The scars of your love re - mind me of us. They keep me
A♭
4fr
B♭
think - ing that we al - most had it all. The scars of your love, they leave me

Gm
3fr
G
Cm
3fr
breath - less. I can't help feel-ing we could have had it all.
B♭
A♭maj7
4fr
B♭
Roll-ing in the deep.
You had my heart and
Cm
3fr
B♭
soul 'side of your hand.
And you played
A♭maj7
4fr
To Coda
B♭
it to the beat.

C5
3fr
G5
3fr
3. Ba - by, I have no sto - ry to be told. But
Drums
B♭5
G5
3fr
B♭5
I've heard one on you now I'm gon - na make your head burn.
C5
3fr
G5
3fr
Think of me in the depths of your des - pair.
B♭5
G5
3fr
B♭5
D.S. al Coda
Make a home down there as mine sure won't be shared.

Coda
A♭maj7
B♭
A♭maj7
4fr
Could have had it all.
B♭
Cm
3fr
Rolling in the deep.
B♭
A♭maj7
You had my heart and soul 'side of your hand.
B♭
But you played it with a beating.

N.C.
Throw your soul through ev - 'ry o - pen door.
Drums
Count your bless - ings to find what you look for.
cont. sim.
Turn my sor - rows in - to trea - sured gold. You'll
Cm
3fr
N.C.
pay me back in kind and reap just what you've sown.

Cm
3fr
B♭
We could have had it
A♭maj7
4fr
B♭
Cm
3fr
all.
We could have had it all.
B♭
A♭maj7
4fr
B♭
It all. It all. It all. We could have had it
Cm
3fr
B♭
all.
Roll - ing in the

A♭maj7
4fr
B♭
Cm
3fr
deep.
You had my heart and soul
'side of your hand.
1.
B♭
A♭maj7
4fr
And you played it to the beat.
B♭
2.
B♭
Could have had it
And you played
A♭maj7
4fr
A♭
4fr
B♭
Cm
3fr
it, you played it, you played it, you played it to the beat.

Shake It Out

Words & Music by Paul Epworth, Florence Welch
& Tom Hull

F
C
Dm
flesh, but I like to keep some things to my - self.
I like to keep
B♭
Gm
3fr
B♭
my is - sues strong.
It's al - ways dark - est be - fore the
F
dawn. And I've been a fool and I've been blind.
I can nev - er leave the past be -
B♭
F
- hind. I can see no way, I can see no way.
I'm al - ways drag - ging that horse a - round.

Dm
B♭
F
And our love is pas - tured, such a mourn - ful sound. To-night I'm gon - na
'Cause I am done with my grace - less heart. So to-night I'm gon - na
C
Dm
bu - ry that horse in the ground. So
cut it out and then re - start. 'Cause
I like to keep
B♭
Gm
3fr
C
my is - sues strong. But it's al - ways dark - est be - fore the
F
Gm
3fr
dawn. Shake it out, shake it out, shake it out, shake it out, oh, whoa.

Gm
B♭
3fr
Shake it out, shake it out, shake it out, shake it out, oh, whoa. And it's hard to dance with a
Gm
F
devil on your back. So shake him off, oh, whoa.
Dm
B♭
And it's hard to dance with a devil on your back. (Shake him off.)
F
C
And given half the chance would I take any of it back.

Dm
B♭
It's a fine ro - mance, but it's left me so emp - ty. (Shake it off.)
Gm
B♭
F
It's al - ways dark - est be - fore the dawn. (Oh, whoa,
oh whoa.)
Gm
Dm
And I'm damned if I do and I'm damned if I don't. So here's to drinks in the dark at the

C
Gm
3fr
end of my road.
And I'm ready-y to suf-fer and I'm ready-y to hope.
Dm
C
B♭
It's a shot in the dark and right at my throat. 'Cause look-ing for heav-en, for the
Dm
C
dev-il in me...
Look-ing for heav-en, for the dev-il in me... Well,
Gm
3fr
F/A
B♭
C
what the hell, I'm gon-na let it hap-pen to me, yeah!

F
Gm
3fr
Shake it out, shake it out, shake it out, shake it out, oh, whoa.
Gm
3fr
Shake it out, shake it out, shake it out, shake it out, oh, whoa.
B♭
Gm
3fr
And it's hard to dance with a dev - il on your back. So shake him off,
F
oh, whoa.

F
Gm
F
Ooh, ooh, ooh, ooh.
B♭
Gm
F
Ooh, ooh, ooh, ooh.
Gm
F
Gm
Ooh, ooh, ooh, ooh.
B♭
Gm
F
Ooh, ooh, ooh, ooh.

She's So Lovely

Words & Music by Roy Stride

Dm
G
C
F
Dm
G
way she fills her clothes, she looks just like them girls in Vogue.
way she bites her lip, I love the way she shakes them hips.
C
F
Dm
G
C
F
I love the way she plays it cool, I think that
I love the way she makes me drool, I think that
Dm
G
C
C
she is beau - ti - ful.
she is beau - ti - ful.
She's so lov - e - ly,
F
Dm
G
C
she's so lov - e - ly, she's so lov - e - ly, she's so lov - e - ly.
She's so lov - e - ly,
She's so lov - e -

F
Dm
G
she's so lov- e - ly,
she's so lov- e - ly.
-ly, she's so lov- e - ly, she's so lov- e - ly.
She's
A
C
F
Dm
pret - ty, a fit - ty, she's got a boy-friend though and that's a
stun - ner, I want her, was she this fit when she was ten years
G
C
F
pit - y. She's flirt - y, turned thir - ty, ain't
young- er? Come see me, dis - creet - ly, she
Dm
G
F
that the age a girl gets real - ly dirt - y?
says she's got a trick or two to teach me.
I don't know,

C/E
Dm7
C
I don't know,
I don't know
how we'll make it through this.
1.
F
C/E
Dm7
C
I don't know,
I don't know,
I don't know.
2.
F
C/E
Dm7
I don't know,
I don't know,
I don't know
C
F
C/E
how we'll make it through this.
I don't know,
I don't know,

Dm7
C
C
F
I don't know.
I think that
Dm
G
C
F
Dm
G
(2°) You
you are love - ly,
I think that
you are love - ly.
C
F
Dm
G
C
F
are
You
are,
I think that
you are love - ly,
I think that

1.
2.
Dm
G
C
you,
you are love - ly.
you are beau - ti - ful.
gliss.
C
F
Dm
G
She's so lov - e - ly, she's so lov - e - ly, she's so lov - e - ly, she's so lov - e - ly,
She's so lov e - ly, she's so lov e - ly, she's so lov e - ly.
she's so lov - e - ly, she's so lov - e - ly, she's so lov - e - ly.

F
C/E
Dm7
C
I don't know,
I don't know,
I don't know
how we'll make it through this.
F
C/E
Dm7
C
I don't know,
I don't know,
I don't know
how we'll make it through this.
F
C/E
Dm7
C
I don't know,
I don't know,
I don't know
how we'll make it through this.
F
C/E
Dm7
C
I don't know,
I don't know,
I don't know
how we'll make it through this.

F
C/E
Dm7
C
I don't know, I don't know, I don't know.
Oh.
Oh oh oh oh oh oh oh oh oh oh oh oh oh oh oh oh.
Oh.
Oh oh oh oh oh oh oh oh oh oh oh oh oh oh oh oh.
Oh.
Oh oh oh oh oh oh oh oh oh oh oh oh oh.

You're Beautiful

Words & Music by Sacha Skarbek, James Blunt
& Amanda Ghost

B♭11/D
(D11/F♯)
Cm7
(Em7)
A♭9
(C9)
E♭
(G)
B♭11/D
(D11/F♯)
My life is bril - liant, my love is pure.
Cm7
(Em7)
A♭9
(C9)
I saw an an - gel, of that I'm sure. She smiled
E♭
(G)
B♭11/D
(D11/F♯)
3
at me on the sub - way, she was with an - oth - er man. But I

Cm7
(Em7)
won't lose no sleep all night, 'cause I've got a plan.
Ab9
(C9)
Bb11/D
(D11/F#)
Eb
(G)
1, 2. You're beau - ti - ful.
3. You're beau - ti - ful.
You're beau - ti - ful.
You're beau - ti - ful.
You're beau - ti - ful, it's true.
You're beau - ti - ful, it's true.
I saw
There must
your face in a crowd - ed place,
be an an - gel with a smile on her face

Cm7
(Em7)
A♭9
(C9)
B♭sus4
(Dsus4)
B♭11/D
(D11/F♯)
E♭
(G)
To Coda II
To Coda I
and I don't know what to do, 'cause I'll nev - er be with you.
when she
Yes, she caught my eye as I walked on by. She could

Cm7
(Em7)
A♭9
(C9)
B♭11/D
(D11/F♯)
see from my face that I was fuck-ing high. And I
E♭
(G)
B♭11/D
(D11/F♯)
don't think that I'll see her a-gain, but
Cm7
(Em7)
D.S. al Coda I
we shared a mo-ment that will last till the end.
Coda I
E♭
(G)
A♭9
(C9)
Cm7
(Em7)
La la la la.

D.S. al Coda II
A♭9
(C9)
Cm7
(Em7)
F7sus4
(A7sus4)
B♭11/D
(D11/F♯)
La la la la. La la la la la.
Coda II
B♭sus4
(Dsus4)
E♭
(G)
thought up that I should be with you.
But it's time to face the truth:
I will nev - er be with you.

Walking On Sunshine

Words & Music by Kimberley Rew

F
E♭
B♭
E♭
and I just can't wait
and I don't wan - na spend
F
E♭
till the day when you knock down the door!
my whole life just a wait - ing for you!
B♭
E♭
F
E♭
Now,
Now, I
B♭
E♭
F
E♭
ev - 'ry time I go for the mail - box, got - ta hold my - self down,
don't want you back for the week - end, not back for a day.
6fr
8fr

B♭
6fr
E♭
6fr
F
8fr
E♭
6fr
'cause
I said,
B♭
E♭
F
E♭
I just can't wait till you write me you're com - ing a - round.
ba - by I just want you back, and I want you to stay.
B♭
E♭
F
E♭
I'm walk - ing on sun -
Dm/F
E♭
- shine, whoa. I'm walk - ing on sun -

Dm/F
E♭
6fr
- shine, whoa. I'm walk - ing on sun -
Dm/F
E♭
B♭
6fr
- shine whoa; and don't it feel good!
To Coda
1.
B♭
E♭
F
E♭
6fr
8fr
Hey, al - right now, and don't it feel good!
B♭
E♭
F
E♭
Hey, yeah! 2. I

2.
B♭
E♭
F
E♭
6fr
8fr
don't it feel good! Yeah, oh, yeah, and
don't it feel good!
E♭/F
Walk - ing on sun - shine.

E♭/F
B♭
E♭
F
E♭
Walk - ing on sun - shine.
E♭/F
B♭
E♭
I feel a - live, I feel a - live, I feel the love
F
E♭
E♭/F
B♭
E♭
that's real - ly real! I feel a - live, I feel a - live,
F
E♭
B♭
I feel the love that's real - ly real! I'm on sun -

B♭
6fr
E♭
6fr
F
8fr
E♭
6fr
- shine, ba - by. Oh, oh, yeah, I'm on sun -
B♭
6fr
E♭
6fr
F
8fr
E♭
6fr
- shine, ba - by. Oh, I'm
D.S. al Coda
Coda
E♭
6fr
B♭
6fr
E♭
6fr
walk - ing on sun -
don't it feel good!
ad lib. vocal
Repeat ad lib. to fade
F
8fr
E♭
6fr
E♭/F
8fr

1 2 3 4 5 6 7 8 9